May God [...]
to you an[...]
your new
family.

Love
Cheryl & [...]tona

A poem by
Harry Behn

◆

Illustrated by
James Endicott

A TRUMPET CLUB SPECIAL EDITION

TREES

Trees are the kindest things I know,

They do no harm,
they simply grow

And spread a shade
for sleepy cows,

And gather birds among their boughs.

They give us fruit in leaves above,
And wood to make our houses of,

And leaves to burn on Hallowe'en,

And in the Spring
new buds of green.

They are the first when day's begun
To touch the beams of morning sun.

They are the last
    to hold the light
When evening changes
    into night,

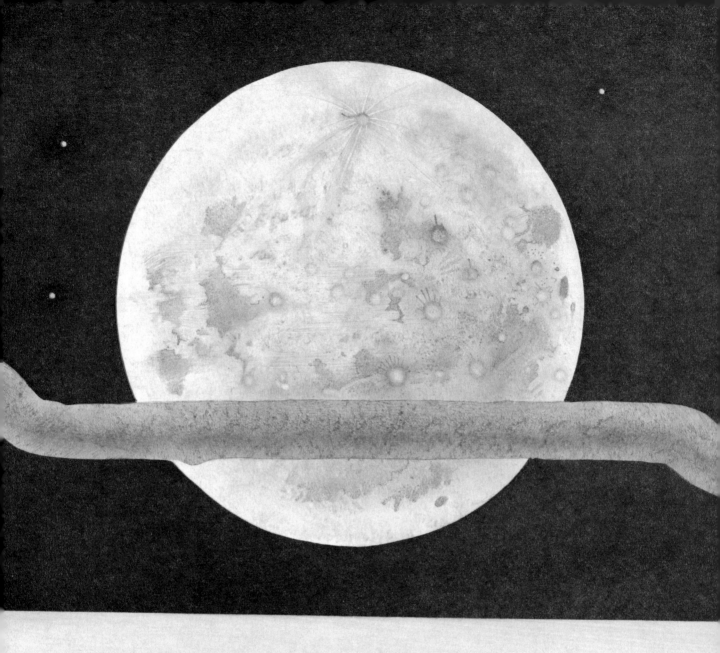

And when a moon floats on the sky

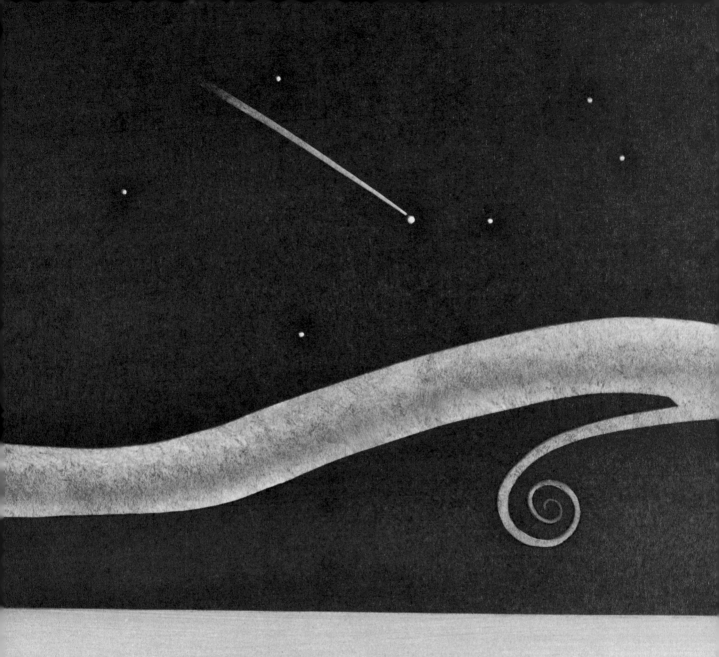

They hum a drowsy lullaby
Of sleepy children

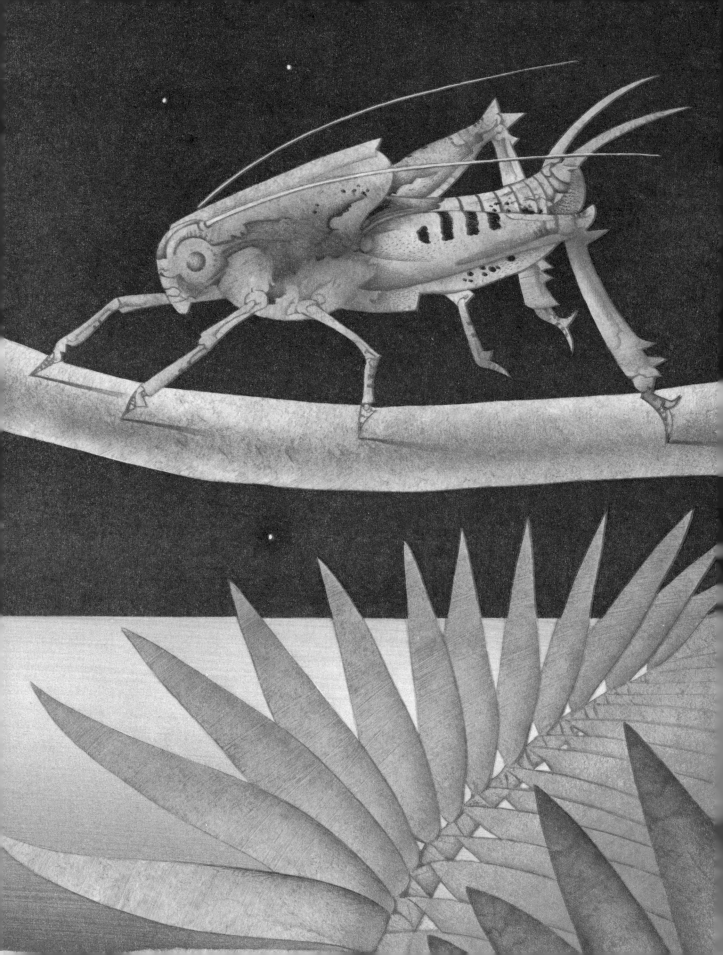

long ago . . .

Trees are the kindest things I know.

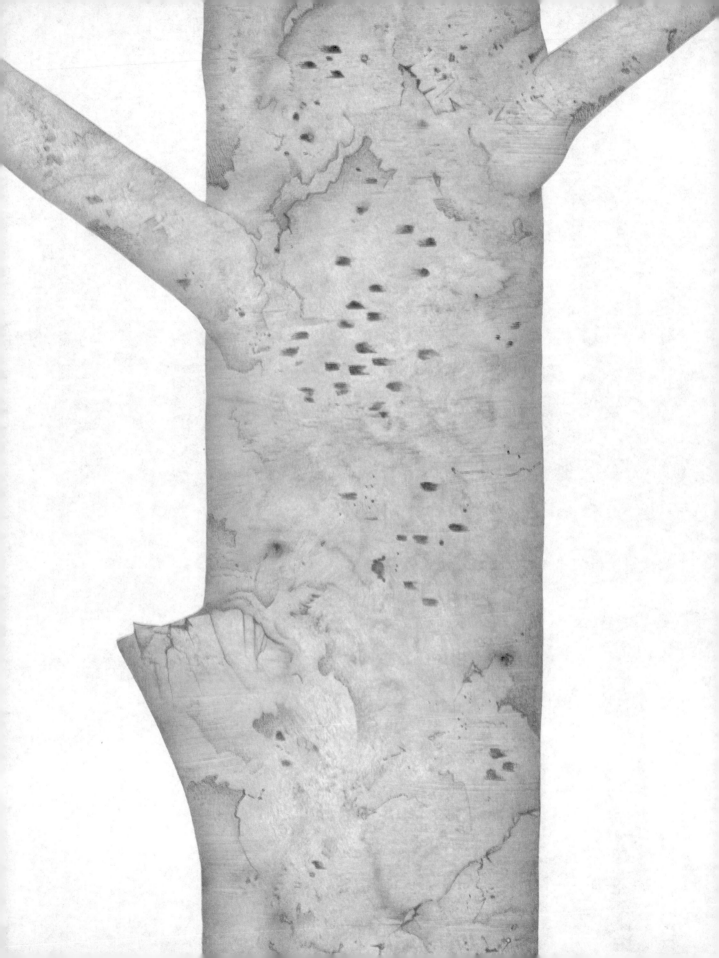

Bill Martin Jr, Ph.D., has devoted his life to the
education of young children. *Bill Martin Books* reflect
his philosophy: that children's imaginations are
opened up through the play of language, the imagery
of illustration, and the permanent joy of reading books.

Published by The Trumpet Club, Inc.,
a subsidiary of Bantam Doubleday Dell
Publishing Group, Inc.,
1540 Broadway, New York, New York 10036.
"A Trumpet Club Special Edition" with the portrayal
of a trumpet and two circles is a registered trademark of
Bantam Doubleday Dell Publishing Group, Inc.

Text copyright © 1949 by Harry Behn, © 1977 by Alice L. Behn
Illustrations copyright © 1992 by James Endicott

ISBN 0-440-83290-X

This edition published by arrangement with
Henry Holt and Company, Inc.

Printed in the United States of America
September 1995
10 9 8 7 6 5 4 3 2
UPR